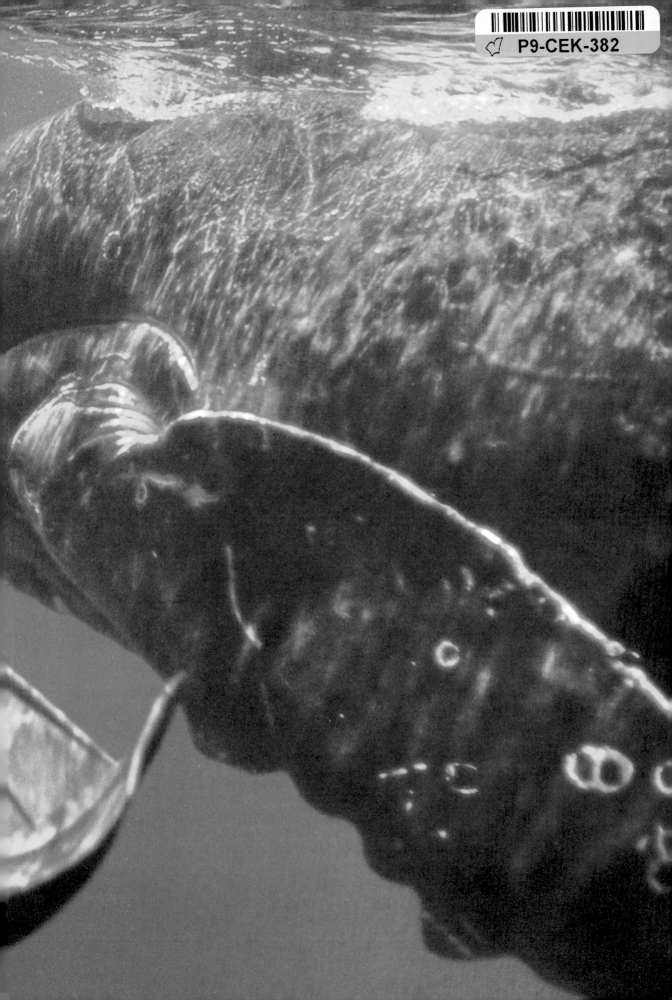

This book was devised and produced by
Multimedia Publications (UK) Ltd.

Editor: Richard Rosenfeld
Assistant Editor: Sydney Francis
Production: Arnon Orbach
Design: Michael Hodson
Picture Research: Vivien Adelman

First published in the United States of America 1985 by Gallery Books, an
imprint of W. H. Smith Publishers Inc., 112 Madison Avenue,
New York, NY 10016

ISBN 0 8317 9408 9

Origination by D S Colour International Ltd, London
Printed in Spain by Cayfosa, Barcelona
Dep. Leg. B-11957-1985

WHALES

Endpapers: *Many whale species are extremely gentle,
posing no threat at all to divers.*

Above/Over: *A performing killer whale at Sea World in Florida.*

Contents page: *The awesome sight of a whale's tail rising
from the surface of the ocean.*

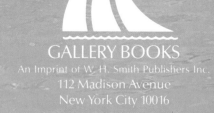

GALLERY BOOKS
An Imprint of W. H. Smith Publishers Inc.
112 Madison Avenue
New York City 10016

WHALES

MICHAEL BRIGHT

Contents

Chapter 1

Whale Fact File

The great whales are the giants on our planet. The blue whale, for example, is the largest creature ever known to have lived. It is larger than the largest dinosaur and bigger than the biggest elephant. The greatest specimen reliably measured was 105 ft (32 m) from the tip of its snout to the notch between its tail flukes, and it weighed 200 tons. The heaviest elephant ever recorded weighed in at under 11 tons – the whale weighed almost 20 times more.

Thick coat

One of the major characteristics of the whale is blubber, the layer of fatty tissue that lies beneath the thinner outer skin. Blubber has two uses – it keeps the whale warm and stores fat. Many whales spend a great deal of time in polar seas, and the insulating layer of blubber, which may be many inches thick, helps keep in their body heat. During courtship, mating and calving in tropical waters, and during migration, some species fast for half the year eating no fish at all for six months – the blubber, rich in stored fats, keeps them going.

When whales arrive back in the nutrient-rich polar seas they have a significantly thinner layer of blubber than when they left. Whales that live all year round in good feeding areas, as do the fin whales that station themselves off eastern Canada, do not put on thick layers of blubber even though they live in cold waters. Clearly they do not need vast reserves of fat as they are always able to feed. What little blubber they do put on is used to keep them warm.

Whales are born without blubber, so have to put it on very quickly before they move to the cold-water feeding grounds with their mothers. Whale milk is so rich that calves gain extra inches in just a few weeks. It has been estimated that, for its first six months, a blue whale calf gains weight at the rate of 8½ lbs (3.85 kg) an hour! It receives 130 gallons (590 liters) of milk a day in about 40 feedings from its mother – equivalent to what the average household consumes in a year.

Rearing whales

The early life of the right whale makes a particularly interesting study. Each year southern right whales visit the Peninsula Valdés in Argentina, and in mid-winter the calves, 18 ft (5.5 m) long, are born in the shallow, sheltered bays in the area. The mother has a single calf that will remain close to her for up to 14 months, 4 of those spent in the bay. Nobody has seen a right whale being born but it is believed to enter the world tail first. It is then helped to the surface to take its first breath. The mother's nipples, as in all other mammals, are underneath, so the baby must learn to dive below in order to receive its supply of milk.

Whales are drawn to Antarctica because of the vast supplies of krill; they are protected from the intense cold by their thick supplies of blubber.

The growing calf is quite boisterous. It practices diving, breaching and rolling, pausing sometimes to rest on its mother's back. The mother is often the center of high jinks but she never responds with a disciplinary slap. She simply endures the butting and the covering of her blowhole with the calf's tail, and rolls over to embrace it with her flippers. Learning to slap with the flippers is, however, important to the calf both for communication and for frightening away killer whales. A mother and her calf form a solitary pair, rarely mixing with others – although many pairs may be found in a bay in what might be termed a "loose" herd.

Preparing for adulthood

In November the mother encourages her calf to firm up its muscles by swimming rapidly up and down the bay. This prepares it for the journey to the feeding grounds in mid-ocean. The calf stays with the mother throughout the rest of the year, returning once again to Peninsula Valdés the following winter. It is gradually weaned. As a yearling, the calf is not protected so much by its mother, and if it ventures away the mother does not go after it. Eventually the mother heads out to sea, leaving the calf to join with other youngsters in small groups. The mother spends an entire year feeding in order to build up the body reserves that she lost bringing up her calf. Female right whales give birth to a single calf approximately every three years.

Deep divers

Whales are mammals and must therefore return to the surface at regular intervals in order to take in lungfuls of air. As, say, a large fin whale surfaces, the snout appears, then the blowhole, the rest of the back and

Above: *A baby gray whale is fitted with a streamlined, light-weight backpack containing a waterproof radio transmitter. It is designed to interfere as little as possible with the whale's everyday life. Each time the whale surfaces bleeps are beamed to researchers following in a boat, enabling them to follow its movements.*

Some species of whale seek out sheltered bays and lagoons in which to mate and give birth. Each winter, southern right whales (left) in the Atlantic Ocean swim to the almost landlocked bays enclosed by Peninsula Valdés on the coast of Patagonia in southern Argentina. Gray whales (below) head for the shallow lagoons of Baja in California.

finally the tail. During this quick movement the body is arched and an upward flexing of the tail pushes the whale back down below the surface. In the couple of seconds that the blowhole is at the surface a large whale is able to expel air from its lungs and take down over 500 gallons (2270 liters) of fresh air.

In humans, only a small proportion, about 15 per cent, of air in the lungs is exchanged in one breathing movement; in whales the figure is nearer 90 per cent. They have perfected the art of taking a quick breath, but must then hold that breath while under the sea. Highly trained pearl divers can hold their breath for about 2½ minutes, hippos for 15 minutes and beavers for 20. The great whales may be down for 40 minutes, sperm whales for 90, and the beaked whales for up to two hours!

Whales are able to hold their breath for so long under water through the presence of a dark red substance called myoglobin in their muscles. Myoglobin stores oxygen until it is needed by the muscles, thus enabling the whale to take sufficient oxygen for its deep dives. It is believed that whales can also divert blood containing oxygen to organs such as the brain and swimming muscles. During deep dives the heart rate slows down by a third to reduce the amount of oxygen used.

Swimming for their lives

Whales are powerful swimmers. With an up-and-down movement of the tail, the great whales can reach a sufficient speed to leap clear of the water. Some have been reported to tow large boats. The large blue and fin whales can cruise at about 5 knots (9 km per hour), swim at 14 knots (26 km per hour) when in a hurry, and zip away at 20 knots (37 km per hour) when escaping danger. The more slender sei whales can reach speeds of 35 knots (65 km per hour) in short bursts.

Far left: *A humpback whale "spy-hopping" – pushing its head right out of the water and having a good look around.*
Bottom right: *A humpback whale swimming belly-up off the coast of Massachusetts. It shows the white underside and the folds of blubber known as throat pleats. These allow an enormous expansion of the mouth cavity when the whale is feeding.*

Below: *A southern right whale "breaching". About 80 tons of whale is lifted almost clear of the water and crashes down in a flurry of spray. Some researchers believe the behavior is a form of communication, particularly in a rough, wind-blown sea when conventional vocal sounds would be inaudible. Others think the whales are just being exuberant since this is mainly practised by youngsters.*

"Thar she blows!"

The blow, or spout, represents both life and death for the great whales. The violent expulsion of air is a vital part of the breathing cycle, but it also signals to whalers that their quarry is near.

Each species of whale has its own distinctive spout. The spout of the right whale, for example, is V-shaped. Spouts are not always visible; but on windy days, when the water is rough, more water is around the blowhole which turns to spray as the whale exhales violently. When traveling at speed, right whales breathe out underwater; they then need spend only a minimum of time at the surface snatching a breath.

The rorquals have a single plume, but only the skilled whaler can recognize the spout of each species. And when, on the old whaling vessels, a spout was sighted, be it the angled left-side plume of a sperm whale or the high geyser of the blue whale, up would go the triumphant cry, "Thar she blows!"

Whale talk

Most whale species are vocal. Blue whales produce very loud and deep moans that have been described as "the most powerful sustained utterances known from whales or any other living source". The notes drop gradually in pitch in a series of moans, and their arrangement is very complex. Blue whales are also thought to be capable of producing high-frequency sounds. The smaller minke whales produce bursts of low-frequency sounds known as "thump trains". Gray whales make a series of clicks, rasps and gong-like sounds. Mothers and calves of this species spend a considerable amount of time "talking" to each other. Right whales make a deep bellowing sound, not dissimilar to that of cows, which is sometimes interspersed with high-frequency chirps. Many whale experts believe that these sounds convey

The blowhole of a humpback whale (top), *and the spout of a southern right whale* (above). *Note the callouses on the head of the right whale, the "coaming" in front of the nostrils and the "post blowhole island" behind. Between the blowhole and the snout of a fin whale* (left) *is a long ridge.*

Fin whales are known to make loud, low-frequency sounds of almost pure tone that can be heard hundreds of miles away under the sea. These whales are usually spotted swimming in pairs, but it could be that each pair is part of a gigantic herd, spread across the ocean, and that the sounds are from individuals in the widely dispersed group trying to keep in contact with one another. Such "conversations" are easily interrupted by the throbbing of supertanker engines.

13

information to other whales about individual and species identity, sex and location.

On their tropical breeding grounds, humpback whales have been heard to sing. The songs are modulated, like those of birds, and they can go on for hours. They have been detected on hydrophones at distances of up to 100 nautical miles (160 km). Only the male sings, presumably either to attract a mate or to warn other males to keep away. The songs, though, have been studied intensively and it has been found that at any given time during the season all the whales in a specific population are singing exactly the same song.

The song does not remain the same throughout the season, but constantly changes. It is probable that a dominant animal in the population rings the change and all the others follow suit. The song can last for anything between five and thirty minutes and, if uninterrupted, an individual might sing without a break for many hours. When a male surfaces to breathe, it does not deliberately stop singing but chooses a natural pause in the song to snatch a breath. During the season the pitch of the songs deepens until the sounds are so low that they cannot be heard, just felt.

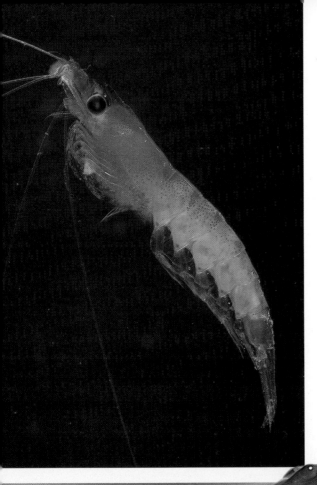

The music of love

A singing whale is almost always alone, separated by several hundred meters from any other singer. If a singer is approached by another whale, probably a female, he stops singing and swims along with her. Sometimes a singer will spot a cow with her calf and head towards her. If she is receptive, and not already mated, the singer stops singing and becomes her escort.

Humpback whales live in separate populations in the different oceans and seas of the world. Around Glacier Bay, Alaska, the north Pacific whales (far left) *spend the summer feeding on small fish and krill* (left).
    These little shrimp-like creatures feed on the abundant plankton floating in the rich Antarctic waters, and can grow from about 2 in (5 cm) to 6½ in (16 cm) in length within the short Antarctic summer. They become so numerous that huge swarms more than a mile long form near the surface, each containing several million tons of krill. The whales graze their way steadily through the swarms of krill (below), *exposed by the melting sea ice.*

Cow, calf and escort will then swim slowly together. Every now and again the cow and male escort dive into the depths of the sea, leaving the calf at the surface. It is believed that this is when they mate.

After a while they both return and the trio continues along at a fairly leisurely pace. Often another singer will see the group, stop singing and approach. This second escort will fight with the first escort for the privilege of swimming next to the female. They blow bubbles at one another, butt their heads together and slap each other with their long flippers. The speed at which the group swims gradually increases. Other singers, attracted by the noise, also approach the group and join the melée. Eventually, the males become bored and swim away, once again taking up their singing positions in the ocean well away from any other whale.

Mating in whales must be a great but delicate affair. Male southern right whales are very gentle. Several males might jostle for a female's attention, but there is little hostility between them. The female rebuffs unsuccessful suitors by lying belly up in the water. The amorous males wait patiently until she runs out of air and is forced to turn over. At this point they swim in and jostle for the best position to mate.

Humpback whales "breaching" (left) and swimming (below). These whales evolved into their distinctive shape about 50 million years ago. At that time, though, they still had legs and would have made excursions onto the land. The fossils of primitive whales have been found in Pakistan, not almongst deep sea creatures, but with the fossils of crocodiles, turtles, catfish and other estuary animals.

These early whales had ears similar to those of land-based mammals and had not, at that stage, developed specialized undersea hearing. The immediate ancestors of whales were thought to be wolf-like carnivores.

Chapter 2

The Great Killers

The most notorious whale – the killer whale – is actually a dolphin whose reputation for ferocity belies its often gentle behavior. Because of this, there is a movement afoot to have the killer whale rechristened orca, after its family name *Orcinus orca*.

Killer whales are the largest and fastest of the dolphins. Males may grow beyond 26 ft (8 m) and females beyond 23 ft (7 m). They are capable of moving through the water at 30 knots (55 km per hour). Killers are black and white and have a grey saddle behind the dorsal fin. In the male this fin is upright and triangular and can grow to 6 ft (1.8 m); in the female the dorsal fin is a little smaller and slightly backward curving.

Killers live in family groups, known as pods, with up to 40 whales per pod. Pods tend to stay together for life, although a very large pod may split into two.

Hunting in packs

Hunting among killers is a cooperative affair, though the adults and older juveniles do all the work with the youngsters just in attendance. In the waters around Vancouver, Canada, where killer whales have been closely studied, Pacific salmon are a favorite food. The killers line up and coordinate themselves with a series of whistles, honks and squawks and herd the fish towards the rocky shore where they will be trapped. They do this by slapping the water with their flippers and flukes, and by leaping clear of the water and belly-flopping back. Then the fish are picked off one by one until the pod is satisfied. Occasionally, killers that have fed well will tease their prey, just as a cat plays with a mouse.

No danger to man

Killers are found all over the world but are far more common in colder latitudes where food – in the form of squid, sharks and other fish, seabirds, penguins, seals and sea lions, other dolphins and large whales – is more abundant. Killers are the only toothed whales to actively prey upon other mammals, but they have rarely put man on the menu. On occasions killers have been known to rise, with their heads out of the water, to peek at the occupants of small boats – but they frequently ignore people who have fallen overboard. In captivity they tend to be gentle and playful.

There are some interesting recorded cases of how killers have behaved when they have come face to face with humans. In 1911 H.L. Ponting, the photographer on Captain Scott's Antarctic expedition, was standing on an iceflow when it was rammed by a couple of killers. This could have been a case of mistaken identity, for killers will often try to upset an iceflow occupied by seals or penguins in order to tip them into the water.

In 1956, off the coast of British Columbia, two

The dorsal fin of a killer whale rises ominously above a steel gray sea.

lumberjacks were putting logs into the water. One of them deliberately set a log to ram one of a group of killers nearby. The whales left the area but returned when the lumberjacks were rowing back to camp. The whales capsized the boat and the man who had upset them was never seen again. His companion was unharmed and lived to tell the story.

During a skindiving competition along the Californian coast in 1962 a group of killers, searching for seals and sealions among the giant kelp beds, approached and checked out each diver in turn before swimming on their way. None of the divers was molested. In 1976, off the coast of Brazil, a large Italian yacht was rammed by

killers. The crew had to swim from the sinking vessel to the lifeboat, but they were totally ignored by the whales, even though they were theoretically "killers".

Where possible baleen whales steer well clear of killer whales. A pack of hungry killers can tear a whale to pieces, although these predators only eat some of the blubber, the skin, the dorsal fin, the tongue and the flesh of the lower jaw. Along the coast of southern California packs of killer whales lie in wait for the arrival of the gray whales, and then take the occasional calf. Killer whales do not often attack adult whales, only juveniles. There is one record of an adult minke whale that got into difficulties in shallow water and was

Killer whales hunting in the surf (left) at Peninsula Valdés, and harassing a group of South American sealions (below). They often swim close-in to the shore in pursuit of their prey but rarely become stranded on the beach.

Killer whales have a large gape (above) with the rows of sharp, backward-pointing, peg-like teeth in the upper and lower jaws interlocking to form a menacing array that can grasp a whole salmon or tear a seal in two. They are voracious predators – one killer was found with the remains of 13 dolphins and 14 seals in its stomach, although they would not all have been eaten during the same feeding session. Killer whales are the only whales regularly to take warm-blooded prey in addition to fish and squid.

less hung around for three hours or so, constantly swimming in and looking for a weak spot. An old or infirm humpback would have been torn to pieces. The killers were typically working as a tight-knit unit.

Ironically, killer whales are the main attraction in marine circuses and are gentle and even friendly to man. In captivity they enjoy being stroked, being admired and being allowed to display their virtuosity of skills. They are popular with both trainers and audiences because they learn fast and perform seemingly impossible tricks.

They are the largest of the performing dolphins and also the most expensive. It has been estimated that many millions of dollars have changed hands in procuring killer whales from the wild. Most are caught near Iceland. The trade is kept very secret, although it is thought that an animal that would have cost about $8000 in 1966 is now valued at over $500 000. Young killer whales are the most sought after as they are easier to train and cheaper to feed. A 10 year old killer whale that lived at Windsor, for instance, ate 175 lb (84 kg) of fish every day.

For the few that make it to dolphinaria there are many that die. Stressed or injured animals, such as those that are held for long periods of time or suffer severe frostbite, are released back into the wild surreptitiously at night. They probably die soon afterwards.

Far left: *A pod (or pack) of marauding killer whales in Glacier Bay, Alaska, stalking a group of humpback whales that visit the bay each summer to feed on the rich "soup" of krill. The male killer is easily recognised by his tall, erect dorsal fin (above).*

Right: *An individual "breaching" in Puget Sound, Washington. Young killers may leap 20 feet (6 m) into the air. They can re-enter the water head-first, causing little disturbance, or come down with an enormous splash. By causing a commotion, killers are able to drive fish, such as salmon, closer to the shore where the prey is trapped and eaten. Often this is a cooperative effort, with all the adult members of the pod executing a military-style "pincer" movement. Large salmon are picked off from the fringes of the school, and there is some evidence that the whales first "zap" the fish with ultrasonic beams to incapacitate them.*

"drowned" by its attackers before it was ripped apart.

A pair of humpback whales were also observed being molested by killer whales off southern Alaska. The biologist's attention was drawn to the humpbacks as they seemed to be chasing a group of killer whales ahead of them. The humpbacks, though, were twisting and turning in the water, and making quite a commotion. Attacking from below and behind was another pack of killer whales, which were attempting to take bites out of the bellies of the humpbacks. The killers were eventually seen off when more humpbacks joined the pair and swam along in a tight formation. The killers neverthe-

Man has been in awe of killer whales from time immemorial. The Romans gave them the name Orca meaning "barrel", and Pliny the Elder wrote in 60 AD about one that was trapped in shallow waters at Ostia, Italy. The Germans call them Schwertwal or "sword-whale", a reference probably to the male's dorsal fin. The Japanese refer to sakamata, which compares the fin to a halberd, a 15th-century weapon that consists of a long scythe-like axe with a pike on the side.

Killer whale bones have been uncovered in ancient garbage dumps, known as "kitchen middens", in Scotland. In southern France pictures of killer whales have been scratched into the walls of caves by primitive man. Today, most people are likely to see killer whales performing, as seen here, in a zoo or aquarium.

Killer whales at Miami (far left) and San Diego (below), and a pilot whale at Redwood City, California (below left). Both species of whales have been used, not only for entertainment, but also for military purposes.

In the US Navy "Deep Ops" program, killer whales Ishmael and Ahab were trained to attach recovery devices to objects on the sea-floor. Unfortunately, they failed to comply. Ishmael made off in a huff, never to be seen again, and Ahab refused to work! Morgan, a captive pilot whale, however, dived to 2000 feet (610 m) and completed all his tasks.

Captive whales have been responsible for destroying the myths that surround killers. They are gentle animals, quick to learn tricks. "You have the distinct feeling, though," wrote one trainer, "that the whale is in charge, and not the trainer!"

The first killer whale to be taken into captivity was at Marineland in 1961. Sadly, it died after just two days. Moby Doll, a male despite its name, was taken from Puget Sound in 1964 and survived three months in Vancouver Aquarium. Namu lived for a year in Seattle Aquarium in 1965. Today there are about 20 captive whales.

When an individual dies it is quickly replaced by another, and sometimes given the same name as its predecessor. Consequently there have been several "Namus" at Sea World in San Diego.

Right and below: *A performing killer putting his trainer through his paces at Sea World in Florida.*

Chapter 3
Long-Distance Voyagers

Thousands of Canadians and Americans flock to the west coast of North America in the spring and fall to see the north and south passage of the migrating gray whales. Tourists packing the lookout points, or on special whale-watch cruises, witness the longest migration of any known mammal. Gray whales may travel 12 500 miles (20 000 km) each year on their round trip from the Arctic to Baja, California. They swim so close to the shore that they can often be seen as they blow at the surface or "spy-hop" – that is, they poke their enormous heads right out of the water in order to check their bearings.

Women and children first

South-bound whales proceed in an orderly manner, seemingly adopting man's code of "women and children first". First are the pregnant females; they race for the shallow lagoons to drop their calves. Next come the recently mated females, then the immature females and finally the adult males.

The northward journey is just as well-planned, with the newly mated females heading for the feeding grounds first to maximize the time that they can feed there. Following them are the adult males, non-breeding females and immature whales. Bringing up the rear are the mothers and their calves.

The biggest danger to the gray whales is the killer whale. Many packs frequent the North American west coast. In order to avoid them, the gray whales swim in towards the shore, hiding behind the giant kelp beds that fringe the Pacific shores.

Traveling companions

It is not certain (because observation in the open ocean is difficult) to what extent whales keep together in tight social groups. Groups varying in number from two to 12 have been seen but on average whales appear to move about in pairs or threes. This could be for feeding purposes. The krill and bait fish, on which the largest whales feed, occur in vast quantities at the ocean surface, but are very patchy. If many single whales converge on a single patch, they would interfere with each other's food intake. There is ample provision for a small group, but too much for an individual. Large groups making a considerable noise attract predators like killer whales and sharks. Solitary whales, chanced upon by a killer pack, might also succumb. Herds of migrating whales minimize the danger of attack by traveling in widely dispersed small groups.

Feeding habits

Between June and October the gray whales and humpback whales of the north-western Pacific live and feed in the Arctic. In spring, as the ice retreats and the

Off on the first stage of a mammoth journey to Baja, California.

Whale watching in the wild. Off the coast of Massachusetts a boat-load of whale-watchers are entertained by a docile humpback (right). And at Baja, California, a tourist (above) and a film-maker (top right) enjoy close encounters with gray whales.

Gray whales can be dangerous, however. They were once known as "devil-fish" for the way that they rammed boats and sometimes broke them up. Females and young ones, though, are known as "friendlies" and often come close to tourist boats where they nuzzle up and allow inquisitive hands to touch and carress their rubbery skin. There was once concern that the frequency of tourist traffic would interfere with the whales' normal way of life but it is thought now that the whales actually enjoy such contact.

nutrients that have settled on the bottom are stirred into growth, there is a superabundance of food. There are plankton "booms" and an enormous increase in the numbers of small fish fry and crustaceans. The food that these whales gather during that period can sustain them for most of the year.

Gray whales feed in shallow waters. They dive to the bottom, turn on their right side and plough with their mouth through the sediment on the sea floor. They extract crustaceans, worms and molluscs. As they ascend they force water through their baleen plates to dislodge the food particles that have collected there. Seabirds, such as glaucous gulls, Arctic terns and horned puffins have taken advantage of this, and wait for the titbits that fall from the whales' mouths.

Killer whales (far right) often lie in wait to ambush gray whales (below) on the migration route to and from Baja and the Arctic. Grays are recognised by the lack of a dorsal fin and from their blotchy grey coloration, the result of numerous spots, scars and patches of barnacles.

Grays have a multitude of names, such as "mussel-digger", on account of their habit of disturbing the bottom sediments and arriving at the surface with mud and debris streaming from the mouth, and "hard-head", from the way that some ram boats. They were hunted to the edge of extinction in the late 19th century but in 1947 gained full protection so that today the population has recovered almost to its former numbers.

Although preoccupied with mating and calfing during their time in the shallow bays of the Baja Peninsula, gray whales do occasionally scour the bottom of the ocean for tasty crabs and shrimps.

Humpback whales have a unique feeding method. It is called "bubble-netting". The whale dives below a shoal of small bait-fish and herring and casts a "net" of bubbles. As the bubbles rise in the water, they form a column that surrounds and ensnares the fish. It is thought that the mesh can be adjusted to hold different size victims by changing the size of the bubbles: as the circle is closed the whale, its mouth wide open, swims up through the center of the column and engulfs the fish. Pleats in the lower jaw swell to accommodate the large quantity of water. The lower jaw is raised and the fish are separated as the water is forced out between the baleen plates. The residue is "licked" from the baleen by the tongue and swallowed.

Humpbacks also indulge in "flick-feeding", during which they splash water over their heads. This disturbs krill for long enough to enable the whale to swim up and gulp them down. Humpbacks also direct krill into their mouths using their very long flippers. They may also "lunge" at small shoals of fish, with six or seven whales advancing abreast; the movements of the whales in the group are coordinated by grunting sounds.

Note the humpback's flippers (below), *which are the longest of any of the whales. They even allow the whales to swim backwards. On the tip of the humpback's snout are protuberances from which bristles grow, although their function is unknown.*

The body is usually blotchy and scarred from barnacles that have dropped off or from the teeth-marks of cookie-cutter sharks. Killer whales also attempt to take chunks out of humpbacks while they are at their summer feeding grounds. The tail of a humpback (left) *shows the distinctive teeth marks of a killer whale.*

Skimmers and gulpers

In general terms, baleen whales fall into two main feeding groups – the "skimmers" and the "gulpers". Bowheads and right whales tend to be skimmers, while the rorquals are gulpers. A blue whale weighing 200 tons will "gulp" up to 8 tons of krill each day. But the same species of whale may not have the same feeding habits in different parts of the ocean; minke whales and fin whales in the north Atlantic and north Pacific, for instance, have slightly different diets from their southern counterparts. Minke whales in the Pacific Ocean eat inshore stocks of saffron cod, while minkes in the Atlantic not only eat fish but are also seen feeding with fin whales that are gulping and sieving krill. Fin whales in the Atlantic eat fish and krill, while the Pacific populations feed on fish, krill *and* squid.

Parasites and predators

The great baleen whales are plagued by parasites and predators. The most curious assailant is the one that leaves small circular bites in the blubber. At one time it was thought that lampreys were responsible, but the culprit has now been identified as the small cookie-cutter shark. It sneaks up on a swimming whale, sinks its large teeth into the skin and blubber, and then allows the forward movement of the whale to twist its own body around until a piece of blubber is bitten off. More dangerous than cookie-cutters are killer whales, or orcas, which attack to kill as their name implies.

Southern right whales, up to 60 feet (18.3 m) long, go sailing (left). They stand on their heads with their tails sticking out of the water at right angles to the wind, enabling them to "sail" across the bay. It seems to be a form of play and the whales will do it for hours on end. Whenever the head bumps on the shore the whales turn about, swim upwind, and then "sail" back again.

Humpback whales (above and right) may reach 50 feet (15.25 m) in length. Each has its own individual pattern of black-and-white patches on the flippers and tail helping researchers to identify and keep track of these long-distance voyagers.

Humpback whales actively feeding (above) *are often accompanied by an excited gaggle of seabirds. Occasionally a bird is accidently swallowed! Humpbacks may communicate with each other on the feeding grounds, but very rarely indulge in bouts of "singing".*

Humpback whales feeding by "bubble-netting". The amount of krill and small fish concentrated inside the rising column of bubbles (below) is far greater than in the surrounding water. A large whale, with mouth wide open, surfaces in the center of its "bubble-net" (left). Two whales (above) have completed their "bubble-net" maneuver and have their throats greatly extended, their mouths brimming with fish and krill. The water is forced out between the baleen plates.

Baleen is made of keratin and grows down from the "gums", but is not a replacement for the teeth that have become vestigial. Baleen first appeared in primitive whales that lived in the sea about 35 million years ago.

Gray whales have the greatest number of parasites. Huge patches of barnacles (below right) are infested with many species of crab-like whale lice (right and below). On one individual over one hundred thousand lice were collected. The lice feed on flaked whale skin and pieces of food that have slurped from the whale's mouth.

The barnacles may be conical ones or the stalked variety, and different species occur on different parts of the whale's body. The stalked barnacles tend to live on top of the conical ones. Sometimes whales enter fresh or brackish waters where the barnacles cannot tolerate the low salinity and drop off. It is thought that "breaching" may also be a way of dislodging parasitic hitch-hikers.

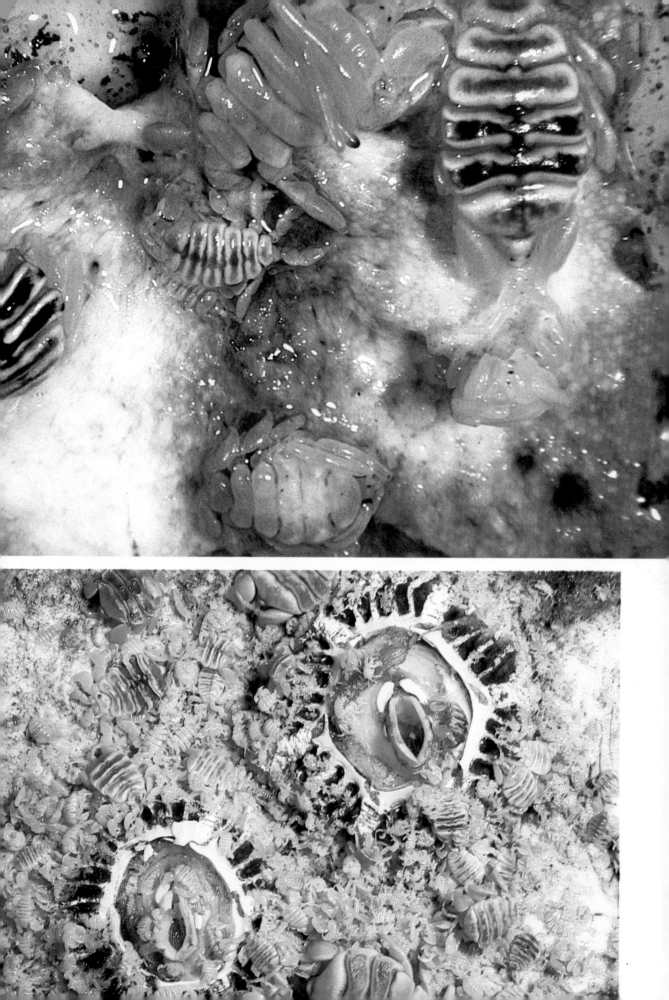

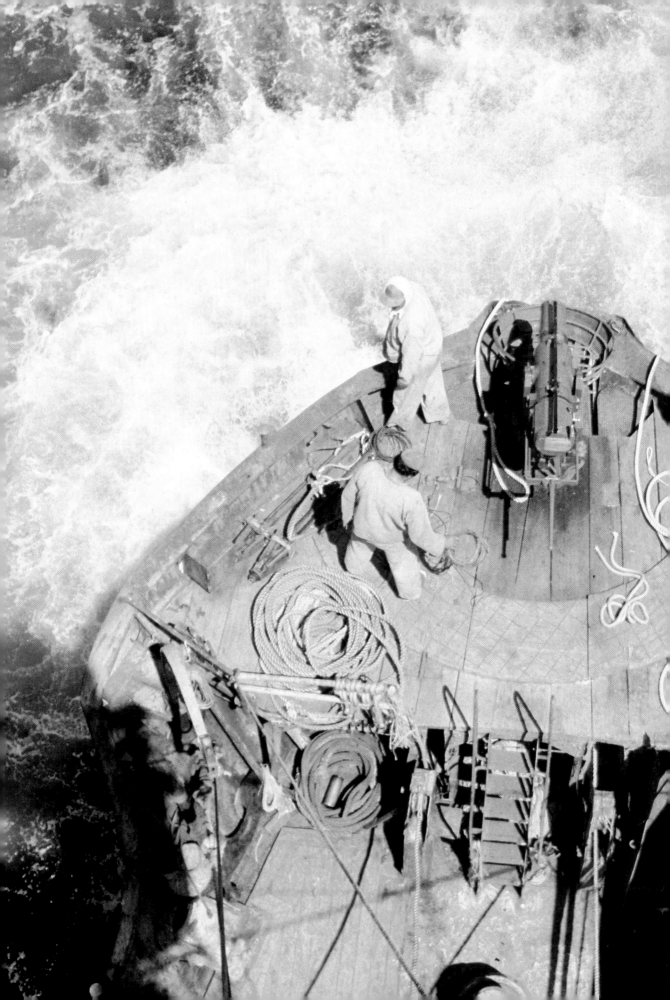

Chapter 4
Fighting to Survive

From time immemorial the coastal peoples of the world have hunted the whale. There are drawings of whales on rocks in Norway that are attributed to primitive artists living in about 2000 BC, and in Alaska archaeological investigations of ancient refuse tips have unearthed whale bones dated about 1500 BC.

Tribal hunters

Early whalers were few in number and were inefficient hunters. Whaling was restricted to those species that lived near the shore. The Eskimo peoples hunted bowhead and northern right whales, and the smaller belugas and narwhals, from single-seat kayaks or 21 ft (6.4 m) long sealskin umiaks crewed by several men. Grays and humpbacks on their migration up and down the Pacific coast of North America were attacked by Indian tribes. The Haida, for example, set out from what is now British Columbia in 35 ft (10.7 m) long cedar dug-out canoes. The harpoon used was made of yew and tipped with the sharp edge of an abalone shell.

In the Aleutian Islands, in the north Pacific, whalers tipped their harpoons with a poison extracted from the monkswood plant. Having speared the whale the hunters would wait until it died, decomposed a little and floated to the surface. Further south, on the other side of the Pacific, the Japanese caught humpbacks in large nets. A swimmer with a long lance would then enter the water to take on the helpless whales.

The death knell sounds

Even when sailing ships enabled whalers to exploit the deep water stocks, and the demand for whale oil was high, the impact on whale numbers was not serious. It was not until the middle of the nineteenth century, when the steamship and the harpoon gun emerged, that hunting began to threaten whale stocks.

Before then, whalers had traveled to the whaling grounds in sailing ships and transferred to rowing boats for the hunt. They would throw hand-held harpoons into the whale, make the line fast to a post on the bows of the rowing boat, and then hang on for their lives as the whale towed them about in the ocean until it tired. They could only take small whales; larger species, such as the blue and fin whales, were left alone.

Foyn's harpoon

The first harpoon guns were mounted on the stems of steamships, which were able to chase the largest of whales. These guns fired barbed harpoons that opened out when embedded in the whale's flesh. Often the harpoon would pull out as the whale dived fast and deep. The whale would later die from its wounds.

Svend Foyn, a Norwegian sea captain, invented the model harpoon gun and explosive harpoon. On its first

The explosive horror of a whale hunt captured from high up in the crow's nest.

49

While modern whaling ships are equipped with the large steel harpoons (right) that are launched from powerful harpoon guns, some "aboriginal" whaling is still carried out with primitive tackle. Around the Azores, in the western Atlantic, whale fishermen go to sea in small open boats propelled by oars or sails. The crew harpoon sperm whales (below) with a simple hand-held spear. A harpooned whale may tow a boat for hours until it tires. The whale is then hauled back to the land where it is sliced up.

test in 1864 the harpoon line caught around his leg and he was pulled into the water. He survived, and a couple of years later perfected his invention which was to decimate the great whale populations of the world and bring the whale to the brink of extinction.

Save the whale

When Foyn's harpoon was fired into the whale's flesh and the barbs began to open, a small glass phial of sulphuric acid broke and a cylinder of gunpowder was ignited. The explosion, except when directly in the brain, did not kill the whale immediately. In great agony the whale would dive deep, occasionally return-

ing to the surface to breathe. When its spout turned red with blood, the whaler knew the end was near. The whale would die writhing in what was euphemistically known as a "flurry".

The dead whale was brought alongside, lanced, and an air-hose was pushed inside its body. The inflated carcass might be towed back to the shore base or factory ship, or left floating in the sea with the company flag pinned on top. Identity notches might be cut in the flukes, ready for the mother ship to collect it later.

Whaling ships today are diesel and equipped with sonar and other devices to make the hunt easier and more efficient. But there are few whales left to catch. A

The controversial "cold grenade" harpoon (below) does not explode inside the whale's body; instead the barbs open up tearing painfully into the flesh. Such killing methods once served large shore stations, like those on South Georgia in the South Atlantic, which have now been abandoned (top right).

Most whales are now caught from catcher boats that serve a factory ship. Catcher boats after minke whales, though, return to shore stations in Norway, and small stations are still used by the whalers operating from the Azores, and St Vincent and St Lucia in the West Indies. Bottom right: As an exhausted whale is overtaken, the Azores harpooner prepares to despatch it with a lance.

regulatory body, the International Whaling Commission, made up of both whaling and non-whaling nations, is attempting to manage whale stocks. There are legal restrictions on the killing of some species.

Though the blue whale was hunted to near extinction – particularly by Norwegian whalers in the north-east Atlantic at the turn of the century – it is now protected, and there are between 7000 and 13 000 left. Humpback and bowhead whales are protected, except for limited aboriginal kills, and their populations stand at 3000–5000 and 2500 respectively. Northern right whales, with an estimated population of 3500, are protected.

Gray whales, also protected, have a stable population in the coastal waters of the north-east Pacific; the western population is virtually extinct. There are less than 88 000 fin whales and 130 000 sei whales; both kinds are only partially protected. Pygmy blue whales can be counted in their hundreds, and are protected. Those that take the burden of the hunt today are Bryde's whales, of which there are thought to be about

80 000 left, minke whales – with a vague estimate of 165 000 to 650 000 surviving – and sperm whales, with over 567 000 surviving.

Sadly, large numbers of whales die each year as a result of human error or negligence as well as from direct violence. For example in the summer of 1984 eight California gray whales died from toxic poisons. Wood preservatives containing harmful chemicals had been decanted into the Serpentine River flowing into the Strait of Georgia earlier in the year and investigations by scientists found that, as a result, the whales had died from acute liver damage.

Ecological upset

Whales have come near to being hunted to extinction because every part of the body is used to make one artifact or another. The consequence of such intensive hunting is a far-reaching ecological imbalance in the areas where whales were once common. In the Southern Ocean, for example, the killing of large numbers of fin

Below: *An enormous fin whale about to be butchered on the dock side.*
Top right: *A sperm whale tooth decorated with scrimshaw, now a collector's piece.*
Bottom right: *Sperm whale blubber is hung up to dry in the sun in   Indonesia.*

Fortunately, most whale products now have viable substitutes. Valuable sperm whale oil, for example, that is used as a high-grade lubricant, can be replaced by the extract of a shrub known as jojoba. This is not a new discovery however: the Apache Indians used it in oil lamps and as a lotion for aching joints.

and blue whales has boosted the krill population. More krill is available to other species. Consequently there has been an increase in the numbers of crab-eating seals, Antarctic fur seals, penguins and other seabirds. Also, the surviving blue and fin whales and smaller whales, like sei and minke whales, are giving birth to their young at an earlier age and at a greater frequency than before.

Before the 1930s, female fin whales matured and had their first calf at about ten years old. Now they mature at six. Minkes have reduced their maturity from fourteen to six years. It is hoped, therefore, that the populations of these whales will bounce back up to their former numbers.

A mass stranding of pilot whales in Tasmania has ended in tragedy (right), and their decaying bodies are buried in the sand (below).

It is thought that the whales, an offshore species unused to negotiating shallow-water obstacles, such as sand banks, were traveling along guided by a magnetic sense "autopilot". With this "sixth-sense" working they could afford to switch off their sonar. Suddenly they hit a "magnetic valley" – a break in the earth's magnetic field – and, caught unawares, ran aground. Inshore species rarely strand: only inshore animals that have died of natural causes are washed up on beaches.

Far left: *Pilot whales are caught in the Faroes, a tradition dating back to Viking times. A ring of small boats encircle the school of whales and, by creating a lot of noise, drive them to the shore where they are hauled up and killed.*

Left: *Migrating humpbacks become entangled in the long drift-nets that criss-cross the seas off Newfoundland. The cod nets are usually destroyed and the whales drown.*

Below: *Holiday-makers attempt to return a school of pilot whales to the sea after they became stranded on a beach in Tasmania. The confused and exhausted whales often beach themselves again and again until they finally swim off.*

When a whale is washed ashore its flesh decays and falls
away, so that all that's left is the gigantic skeleton. Below:
The ribs of a southern right whale. Inset: A collection of
whale bones on the beach of an Antarctic island.

At one time, "whale-bone" was the name given to the
keratinized baleen rods. They ended up in ladies' corsets,
and as umbrella ribs, clock springs, and riding crops.
Bowhead whales have the longest baleen plates, some
growing to 15 feet (4.5m) in length.

Far left: *Minke whales, the smallest of the rorquals, are taking the brunt of modern whale fishing.* Left: *Sperm whales, an adult seen here with a two days old calf, are still fished in small numbers.* Below: *Blue whales are totally protected.*

Blue whales can be distinguished from fin and sei whales by the way the tail comes right out the water before the dive. They have a narrow "blow" that may reach a height of 30 feet (9 m). Blue whales are monogamous and are usually seen swimming in pairs. Very little is known about their numbers or distribution, but the few that have survived are a living proof that there are still giants on this planet.

PICTURE CREDITS